BEYOND THE YELLOW BRICK ROAD:
UNLOCKING THE PROMISES OF GOD

STUDY GUIDE

JUAN MARTINEZ

BEYOND THE YELLOW BRICK ROAD: UNLOCKING THE PROMISES OF GOD STUDY GUIDE

JUAN MARTINEZ

COPYRIGHT

SESSION CONTENTS

Introduction

Welcome to the *Beyond the Yellow Brick Road: Unlocking the Promises of God Study Guide.* I'm so proud of you for taking the necessary steps to care for yourself. This is no time to feel guilty about making sure you are okay. I want you to know that you'll be better than okay because you'll be making tough decisions based on biblical advice.

This workbook, just like the book, relies on God's Word for guiding us through life's storms and into the promises of light. Allow this workbook to help reinforce what it is that the pages of Beyond the Yellow Brick Road: Unlocking the Promises of God have spoken into your life.

As you prepare for the first session, I want to encourage you in three areas:

• **First** - Be committed. If you are committed to God first, you can survive anything and live a blessed life in His light.

• **Second** – Be Bold. Some of the discussion questions may challenge you to talk about important issues. It's normal to feel some resistance when you feel as though you've been hurt or disappointed. However, it's important to acknowledge what's really going on in your heart and mind.

• **Third** - Focus on what you can do. Some discussion questions may present an opportunity to be critical of yourself and others. There will be times when you can honestly say how you feel about important issues. But the key to navigating through wilderness seasons of obscurity is a willingness to focus on what you can do for yourself, and what you can change in you.

The bottom line is that none of us are perfect, and because you're working to restore life to the blessing God intended, doesn't mean you've failed. It means there is a blessed life up ahead.

USING THIS WORKBOOK

Each session of your workbook will include session summaries, fill in the blank and discussion questions. I've also included key Scripture from each chapter to center your focus on the topic.

QUESTIONS

This section of your workbook features fill-in-the blank and multiple-choice questions to help you review key themes from the teaching. Some questions will immediately invoke a memory or emotion. Don't suppress it. Allow yourself to process feelings you may not even realize you're still dealing with.

Other questions may even bring some tension or frustration to the surface. This is normal. When needed, take a break, and revisit the questions later. Be committed to the process of working through this guide. Trust that the result will be a better, more blessed you.

And I will give you the keys of the Kingdom of Heaven.
Whatever you forbid on earth will be forbidden in heaven, and
whatever you permit on earth will be permitted in heaven."
Matthew 16:19

Paving Streets of Gold

Unlocking The Promises of God

Session One

DISCUSSION:

In the months following Hurricane Harvey that hit us in Houston, Texas, I couldn't shake thoughts of how that storm changed our lives. I remembered watching The Wizard of Oz as a kid and how that monster twister zigzagged across the Kansas landscape, kicking up dust and turning Dorothy's world upside-down. A passing thought. No big deal, right?

But one morning as I prayed in the quiet of my office preparing the Sunday message, The Wizard of Oz kept tugging at my spirit, but I didn't know why. It was an old movie, and it had nothing to do with that Sunday's Word. Still, I sat and lingered in prayer. Suddenly, God said, "When you pray, you're releasing heaven into the earth."

His Word dropped into my spirit and settled there. I knew there was more coming, so I pressed in. Yet, nothing. I was like, what else you got for me, Father? But there was only the seed He'd planted: You're releasing earthly cares for a heavenly reality.

As I preached my originally planned sermon, the entire vision of the Yellow Brick Road came spilling out faster than I could contain it. I rolled with it as people began to clap, laugh, and shout, "Amen." I was so excited about what was coming out of my mouth that I was doing the same as the congregation.

God showed me that when we pray, we release heaven—we essentially "pave" the earth with heaven's streets of gold. In my mind's eye, I saw the Yellow Brick Road, and suddenly, everything clicked.

As believers, we're called to "speak life" or to bring heaven down to earth through the Word of God. We bring heaven into the earthly realm by the words we say and the words we pray. It's an exchange of wishes; our desire for his.

Remember the words of the Lord's Prayer? "Thy kingdom come, Thy will be done, on earth as it is in heaven." Jesus intended those words to be so much more than a nice prayer we rattle off before communion.

The Word of God is all-powerful and living, sharper than a two-edged sword. It changes the course of history. It transforms lives. It can even change a wretch like me. The question is, "Have you allowed it to do for you what it has done for me?"

RELATED SCRIPTURES

The twelve gates were twelve pearls, each gate made of a single pearl. The great street of the city was of gold, as pure as transparent glass.
Revelation 21:21

Although [ships] are so large and are driven by strong winds, they are steered by a very small rudder wherever the pilot wants to go. Likewise, the tongue is a small part of the body, but it makes great boasts ... With the tongue, we praise our Lord and Father, and with it, we curse human beings, who have been made in God's likeness. Out of the same mouth come praise and cursing. My brothers and sisters, this should not be. Can both fresh water and saltwater flow from the same spring?
James 3:4-11 NIV

---

9 "This, then, is how you should pray:
" 'Our Father in heaven, hallowed be your name,
10 your kingdom come, your will be done, on earth as it is in heaven.
11 Give us today our daily bread.
12 And forgive us our debts, as we also have forgiven our debtors.
13 And lead us not into temptation, but deliver us from the evil one.
Matthew 6:9-13 (NIV)

LESSON

Fill in the blanks from Pastor Juan's teaching taken from Session 1:

1. As believers, we're called to _____ or to bring heaven down to earth through the Word of God.

2. The Word of God is all-powerful and living, sharper than a two-edged _____. It changes the course of history. It _____ lives.

3. Your personal _____ is a statement of a witness under oath. This means your testimony actually bears _____ of what God has done in your live as we tell the story of how you _____ destruction.

ADDITIONAL NOTES FROM SESSION ONE

Take this opportunity to pray over and think about what was shared in this lesson. Reading is informational but meditating over what was read becomes transformational. Write out your thoughts, observations and questions that may have come up during the lesson. Go back through the chapter or keep this on hand as you work through the book. The time you invest in prayer will also reveal the answers or clarity that you may seek for very personal questions.

DISCUSSION QUESTIONS

1.   Write out in detail your memory of the last life storm you struggled through without God. Once you've written it out in detail, meditate over what you remember about feelings of darkness, depression, and despair. Now, compare that how you would handle the same storm having the peace and comfort of Jesus Christ.

_____

_____

_____

_____

_____

2.   Have you ever written out your personal testimony? It can be hard and even painful as you focus on who you once were without Christ versus who you now are in the Body of Christ. Take your time and write out your testimony as if you were going to read it to someone seeking God. If you feel comfortable sharing it with the group, please ask the leader for a chance to share.

_____

_____

_____

_____

_____

WHAT HAS GOD SAID TO YOU?

Any time we surrender ourselves to the Holy Spirit, there is inspiration or revelation. Has God spoken into your life as you've studied this session? If so, make sure to write it out so you will have a record of His Word and something real to pray over in the coming days.

_____

_____

_____

_____

_____

CALL TO ACTION

What powerful words are you using? Are you calling down heaven or raising up curses with your speech?

_____

_____

_____

_____

_____

SHARE YOUR HEART

Take this time to pray about your relationship with God in in this season of your life. Write out your prayer requests, praise reports and anything you want to step out in faith about. This is your workbook, so write what is on your heart.

_____

_____

_____

_____

_____

_____

_____

_____

_____

_____

_____

_____

_____

_____

_____

_____

_____

_____

_____

_____

_____

_____

_____

_____

God Uses Storms to Get Your Attention

Gaining Perspective from the Pain

Session Two

DISCUSSION

We all have a "storm story," so I want to share some sunshine by going tough love on you for a moment, but it's for your own good. It's important to understand that the mess you find yourself in is because you're complicating God's promise for your life.

Maybe you're going through that storm right now. Maybe it's an addiction or debt, or marriage problems, etc. Maybe you're going through life gripped by fear and doubt. Maybe you need healing from a past relationship, or there is sickness in your body. No matter what you're facing, there is only one way—one road, one Yellow Brick Road— to that place of God's promise.

As a matter of fact, rarely have I met a strong person who doesn't have a storm story. When God uses a storm, His intention is to bring order from chaos and to bring us into alignment with our assignment. In my crazy life, God used a storm to get my attention.

Think about the areas of chaos in your life and consider how God might use these storms to bring about a much-needed change. I was caught in storms called drug addiction, lust, and anger, as well as prison, and God used each of these chaotic situations to bring me closer to my purpose. God will use our mistakes and our circumstances to bring about His greater plan and glory.

We respond to trouble and pain in the same way Dorothy tried to run away from the storm. After all, who really wants to go through a storm? Wouldn't we rather be magically transferred to a place where there is no trouble and be free of pain?

God, on the other hand, uses these opportunities to take us through difficult times so that we can be refined in the fire. It's in those times that our transformation becomes central to becoming the person God wants to use for leading others to Him.

What is God speaking to you out of your current circumstances? The truth is, God is always speaking, and He desires to get your attention. Ever notice how God will use a person, social media or even a random sign to get His message across to you?

If so, do you ignore it, or are you receptive and ready to listen? He's talking to you right now in RED letters. He loves you.

RELATED SCRIPTURES

Do not conform to the pattern of this world but be transformed by the renewing of your mind. Then you will be able to test and approve what God's will is—his good, pleasing, and perfect will.
Romans 12:2

I will give you a new heart and put a new spirit in you; I will remove from you your heart of stone and give you a heart of flesh.
Ezekiel 36:26

Be strong and very courageous. Be careful to obey all the law my servant Moses gave you; do not turn from it to the right or to the left, that you may be successful wherever you go.
Joshua 1:7

LESSON

Fill in the blanks from Pastor Juan's teaching taken from Session 2:

1. The _____ you find yourself in is because you're complicating God's _____ for your life.

2. During a _____, we might think we are losing everything because we misplace our identity in things not of Christ; but in reality, we are _____ losing anything.

3. No matter what you're facing, there is only one way—one road, one Yellow Brick Road—to that place of _____ promise.

ADDITIONAL NOTES FROM SESSION TWO

Take this opportunity to pray over and think about what was shared in this lesson. Reading is informational but meditating over what was read becomes transformational. Write out your thoughts, observations and questions that may have come up during the lesson. Go back through the chapter or keep this on hand as you work through the book. The time you invest in prayer will also reveal the answers or clarity that you may seek for very personal questions.

DISCUSSION QUESTIONS

1.Have you ever felt like God abandoned you in a stormy season of life? If so, describe what caused those feelings and what your heart was telling you about why you felt that way. What did you learn through the experience?

_____

_____

_____

_____

_____

2. Describe your last serious break through. Was it a struggle in overcoming addiction, divorce, debt? We all pass through tough times, so explain what yours was and how God carried you through. Include what you see as the new beginning or calling in your life.

_____

_____

_____

_____

_____

WHAT HAS GOD SAID TO YOU?

Any time we surrender ourselves to the Holy Spirit, there is inspiration or revelation. Has God spoken into your life as you've studied this session? If so, make sure to write it out so you will have a record of His Word and something real to pray over in the coming days.

_____

_____

_____

_____

_____

CALL TO ACTION

What will it take for God to get your attention? Have you asked God to do just that?

_____

_____

_____

_____

Count It All Joy

When God has Other Plans…

Session Three

DISCUSSION

Although we lost everything in Hurricane Harvey, God showed me what we still had was actually the most important thing in life – we escaped with our lives. Learning to count even your suffering as joy is pleasing to God.

Did you catch that? Peter said, "after you've suffered a little while." If you're like the old me, you'd rather do without that part about suffering, thank you very much. But over the last years, God has fast-tracked me and taken me on a whirlwind ride like nothing I could have ever dreamed up.

Are you familiar with the term "apprehend?" It's a word used in law enforcement, like when a police officer apprehends a criminal. It means to arrest, seize, grasp, or capture. Well, after living a life on the jagged edge for twenty years by dealing drugs and causing destruction everywhere I went, that's what God did to me. He apprehended me —grasped me out of a life racing headlong toward hell and put me on a new path. On this new path, I was rescued from my storm and healed by Jesus.

God brought my perspective back into alignment with truth: God is our everything. We might fear losing everything because we misplace our identity in things not of Christ. But in reality, we are not losing at all because worldly things are merely material possessions or a relationship that you shouldn't have gotten into.

Would you still rely upon God if you lost every single thing but your life? It's hard to say for some people, but until you're faced with it, you don't really know what your perspective would be.

Unless of course, you cling to Jesus each and every day whether you're in a storm or not.

God uses situations in our life to remind us that He is everything. This was my proving ground, what I like to call a heart check, aka The Test.

God used the reality of losing it all to bring about a greater eternal perspective: He is everything in my life, and storms will always come and go but He will always remain the same.

RELATED SCRIPTURES

And the God of all grace, who called you to his eternal glory in Christ, after you have suffered a little while, will himself restore you and make you strong, firm, and steadfast.
1 Peter 5:10 NIV

Trials and Temptations
2 Consider it pure joy, my brothers and sisters, whenever you face trials of many kinds, 3 because you know that the testing of your faith produces perseverance.
James 1:2-3 (NIV)

LESSON

Fill in the blanks from Pastor Juan's teaching taken from Session 3:

1. The _____ never promises that we won't go through tough times.

2. God will bring your _____ back into alignment with _____.

3. In life, many times, we _____ on the storm and what's on the outside when all that really matters is what's on the inside—the real _____.

ADDITIONAL NOTES FROM SESSION THREE

Take this opportunity to pray over and think about what was shared in this lesson. Reading is informational but meditating over what was read becomes transformational. Write out your thoughts, observations and questions that may have come up during the lesson.

Go back through the chapter or keep this on hand as you work through the book. The time you invest in prayer will also reveal the answers or clarity that you may seek for very personal questions.

DISCUSSION QUESTIONS

1. What does James 1:2 mean to count it pure joy? Describe what that really looks like when life is not going the way you wanted.

_____

_____

_____

_____

_____

2.   Share a time in your life when everything was out of control, but you held true to your faith that God would provide. Describe at what point of the darkness did you first see His light. Did you immediately understand that your feet were on solid ground?

_____

_____

_____

_____

_____

WHAT HAS GOD SAID TO YOU?

Any time we surrender ourselves to the Holy Spirit, there is inspiration or revelation. Has God spoken into your life as you've studied this session? If so, make sure to write it out so you will have a record of His Word and something real to pray over in the coming days.

_____

_____

_____

_____

_____

CALL TO ACTION

When was your last storm in life and what did it teach you about God?

_____

_____

_____

_____

_____

From Black-and-White to Technicolor

It Doesn't Always Look the Way you Want

Session Four

DISCUSSION

I love colors. That's the way God made me, and I'm thankful for that passion for fashion as well as the way colors move me. The distinction of colors used in The Wizard of Oz also moved me as I understood it to signify the different seasons in our lives. Sure, we have phases in life where our reality is the starkness of black-and-white, but once we come into an incredible relationship with Jesus Christ, there is a technicolor explosion of understanding God's truth.

Are you living in a world where the words others speak over you remove God's beautiful colors from your life? Dorothy was similar in that she allowed people in her life to speak the "color" right out of her potential for joy. Even the people closest to Dorothy were anxious to point out her shortcomings. Someone told her she needed to use her brain to confront the problem she was running from. Another person said she just needed to have courage. And finally, her aunt pointed out that she was always worrying about something that was really nothing.

Isn't that like most of us? We get anxious over everything yet pray about nothing. What mattered more than Dorothy's point being pondered was her process for approaching it.

She allowed negative words to occupy her spirit and turn her colorful potential into a drab black-and-white reality.

Dorothy, just like all of us, has a decision to make. How we approach those decisions can be just as important as the decision itself.

She, like we, face many opportunities to make decisions that will affect our internal reality. In her process of seeking truth, Dorothy begins to talk about a place where no trouble exists but that you couldn't get to with a boat or a plane. It was a place somewhere far away.

It was a place somewhere over the rainbow.

RELATED SCRIPTURES

6 Be anxious for nothing, but in everything by prayer and supplication, with thanksgiving, let your requests be made known to God; 7 and the peace of God, which surpasses all understanding, will guard your hearts and minds through Christ Jesus.
Philippians 4:6-7 (NKJV)

Then they cried to the LORD in their trouble, and he delivered them from their distress. He made the storm be still, and the waves of the sea were hushed. Then they were glad that the waters were quiet, and he brought them to their desired haven.
Psalm 107:28-30

LESSON

Fill in the blanks from Pastor Juan's teaching taken from Session 4:

1. Are you living in a world where the _____ others speak over you remove God's beautiful _____ from your life?

2. As _____, we want to see certain _____ come to pass in our lives.

3. We have an adversary, the _____, who wants us to live in _____.

ADDITIONAL NOTES FROM SESSION FOUR

Take this opportunity to pray over and think about what was shared in this lesson. Reading is informational but meditating over what was read becomes transformational. Write out your thoughts, observations and questions that may have come up during the lesson.

Go back through the chapter or keep this on hand as you work through the book. The time you invest in prayer will also reveal the answers or clarity that you may seek for very personal questions.

DISCUSSION QUESTIONS

1. Words really do have power. Have there been curses spoken over you that you have yet to break? Things said like you are a failure, too poor, too dumb, too lazy to ever succeed. So many destructive words burrow into our spirit. Write out a positive affirmation over your life. Don't be shy about it. Pray and listen to what God says about you and then write out those amazing words. Keep hold of them because they are the truth.

_____

_____

_____

_____

_____

2. Do you fully understand and are confident in the reality that through the blood of Jesus Christ, you have the power to resist the devil? Instead of running away the instant he threatens you, confront his lie and face the giants of insecurity, fear, approval from others, addictions, selfishness, worry, etc. That means no running away from things that we should be claiming victory over. Write out a sentence or two that you can and will rely on to counter the devil's false claims against you. Be ready for war.

_____

_____

_____

_____

_____

WHAT HAS GOD SAID TO YOU?

Any time we surrender ourselves to the Holy Spirit, there is inspiration or revelation. Has God spoken into your life as you've studied this session? If so, make sure to write it out so you will have a record of His Word and something real to pray over in the coming days.

_____

_____

_____

_____

_____

CALL TO ACTION

What are you worried about? Are you willing to give it to God and pull down the promises of heaven through faithful prayer?

_____

_____

_____

_____

_____

SHARE YOUR HEART

Take this time to pray about your relationship with God in in this season of your life. Write out your prayer requests, praise reports and anything you want to step out in faith about. This is your workbook, so write what is on your heart.

_____
_____
_____
_____
_____
_____
_____
_____
_____
_____
_____
_____
_____
_____
_____
_____
_____
_____
_____
_____
_____
_____
_____
_____
_____
_____

Storms: God's Agents of Change

Are you Listening?

Session Five

DISCUSSION

Why is it that we think storms are bad? Well, we hear of the destruction they bring, mostly from the media, but also from word of mouth. I want to invite you to look at storms with new eyes. In Luke 8:22-24, we read that Jesus said to His disciples, "Let's cross to the other side of the lake." So, they got into a boat and started out. As they sailed across, Jesus settled down for a nap. But soon, a fierce storm came down upon the lake. The boat was filling with water, and their perspective told them they were in real danger. The disciples woke Jesus up, shouting, "Master, Master, we're going to drown!"

When Jesus woke up, He rebuked the wind and the raging waves. Suddenly, the storm stopped, and all was calm. If we look at this story carefully, we see there's a storm, but I see a promise too. I see Jesus saying, Let's go to the other side. In other words, if Jesus said it that means no storm can stop you. The disciples should have remembered what Jesus said and told the storm to muzzle up; in other words, "Shut up, storm," knowing they were going to the other side. Let's stop complicating God's promises with our solutions!

Last I heard, Jesus took the sting from death. So why panic and freak out about a storm? After all, a storm isn't supposed to bring us to a bad place in our life, even if it leads to death. If we know that our end here on earth is only the beginning of our eternity with Jesus, why do we consider death such a bad thing?

29

Now, don't think I'm suggesting that there should be no compassion or mourning for those who have passed on, but should we not celebrate someone going to glory?

When someone dies, the real concern is whether he or she received salvation through faith in Jesus.

When I scale my life to all of creation, I laugh, realizing how we think our storms are bigger than the universe at times.

I bet if we had a front-row seat to watch the birth of creation, we would have thought it was a storm of mass destruction when really, it was creation forming.

God always brings something good from the storms in our lives. He brings order from chaos.

RELATED SCRIPTURES

22 Now it happened, on a certain day, that He got into a boat with His disciples. And He said to them, "Let us cross over to the other side of the lake." And they launched out. 23 But as they sailed He fell asleep. And a windstorm came down on the lake, and they were filling with water, and were in [a]jeopardy. 24 And they came to Him and awoke Him, saying, "Master, Master, we are perishing!" Then He arose and rebuked the wind and the raging of the water. And they ceased, and there was a calm.
Luke 8:22-24 (NKJV)

But we speak the wisdom of God in a mystery, even the hidden wisdom, which God ordained before the world unto our glory: Which none of the [demonic] princes of this world knew: for had they known it, they would not have crucified the Lord of glory.
1 Corinthians 2:7-8 KJV

LESSON

Fill in the blanks from Pastor Juan's teaching taken from Session 5:

1. I want to invite you to look at _____ with new eyes.

2. If we know that our end here on _____ is only the beginning of our _____ with Jesus, why do we consider death such a bad thing?

3. God always brings something _____ from the storms in our lives. He brings _____ from chaos.

ADDITIONAL NOTES FROM SESSION FIVE

Take this opportunity to pray over and think about what was shared in this lesson. Reading is informational but meditating over what was read becomes transformational. Write out your thoughts, observations and questions that may have come up during the lesson.

Go back through the chapter or keep this on hand as you work through the book. The time you invest in prayer will also reveal the answers or clarity that you may seek for very personal questions.

DISCUSSION QUESTIONS

1. Write out what makes you feel most loved, gives you a sense of security, makes you feel significant and where do you find your purpose. Explore the potential that your answers might have changed since experiencing a serious storm in life.

_____

_____

_____

_____

_____

2. Your storms are meant to bring about transformational change that prepares you for a new anointing in life. Describe what new blessings or spiritual giftings you received because of passing through your latest storm.

_____

_____

_____

_____

_____

WHAT HAS GOD SAID TO YOU?

Any time we surrender ourselves to the Holy Spirit, there is inspiration or revelation. Has God spoken into your life as you've studied this session? If so, make sure to write it out so you will have a record of His Word and something real to pray over in the coming days.

_____

_____

_____

_____

_____

CALL TO ACTION

Describe how the latest storm in your life made you feel? Did you call out to Jesus to bring peace or did you cry out in fear?

_____

_____

_____

_____

_____

Releasing Heaven on Earth

Proclaim God's Promise

Session Six

DISCUSSION

In our lives, as we follow the Yellow Brick Road—as we pray to release heaven on earth—we are essentially walking out the Word of God. This is the only way we can truly overcome. The Word is really His Word. It's not just me saying, "I used to be addicted to drugs, and now I'm free." It's out of our being that we do. I was made free by spending time in His Word and through interacting with His Word.

It's up to us to walk according to His Word for that freedom to be truly experienced in our lives. In other words, we can't just talk about it, we must live it, and we can only live it by dying daily at the cross and allowing His spirit to live in our daily choices. Every yes to a promise of God is a no you have to say to the flesh.

All throughout Scripture, we are told to continually speak the words of God as we walk our lives. We see Jesus quoting such in the New Testament and hear about how the early church lived this out. We are to pray and walk out the promises of God in our lives and the lives of those following after us. We pray the Word and take each step as it becomes illuminated. That's how we get through the storms in our lives and into the promises of God.

Isn't it interesting that the Scarecrow, who needed a brain, the Tin Man, who needed a heart, and the Lion, who needed courage, were all at different places along the path? The Scarecrow wasn't effective in what he was called to be, and he believed he wasn't able to think.

Have you ever felt this way? Do you feel ineffective, or do you have a hard time believing that your mind is valuable? Do you ever feel like you're not smart enough?

I know that was one of my storms. I felt like I was dumb and not smart enough until I realized I could ask God for wisdom, and because we are connected, I'm a genius by default (lol).

What words have stopped you from praying over your life? Can you pinpoint where you might have jumped off the Yellow Brick Road? Are you in a place frozen with hopelessness while chopping wood?

When did you allow indecision to halt your progress forward? Are you stuck like the Scarecrow, nailed to the post of paralysis through analysis? Did you stop walking the path because of fear and a lack of courage? What will it take to get you easing on down that road once again?

RELATED SCRIPTURES

Death and life are in the power of the tongue,
And those who love it will eat its fruit.
Proverbs 18:21 (NJKV)

Whatever you ask in my name, this I will do, that the Father may be glorified in the Son. If you ask me anything in my name, I will do it.
John 14:13-14

LESSON

Fill in the blanks from Pastor Juan's teaching taken from Session 6:

1. As we _____ to release heaven on earth—we are essentially walking out the Word of _____.

2. On that road to _____, a blinding light struck down Saul and his travel companions. The guy was literally knocked off his _____.

3. Sometimes I think <u>God</u> looks down from heaven at His future sons and daughters—the really tough cases like a Saul of Tarsus—and plots these _____ interventions (storms) to turn them around so He can use them for His _____.

ADDITIONAL NOTES FROM SESSION SIX

Take this opportunity to pray over and think about what was shared in this lesson. Reading is informational but meditating over what was read becomes transformational. Write out your thoughts, observations and questions that may have come up during the lesson.

Go back through the chapter or keep this on hand as you work through the book. The time you invest in prayer will also reveal the answers or clarity that you may seek for very personal questions.

DISCUSSION QUESTIONS

1. What words of God have you stopped praying over your life? Why did you stop? Was it someone or something that caused you to abandon God's Word for you? Have you overcome that pause, and if so, how did you accomplish it? If you haven't, what will it take to start again?

_____

_____

_____

_____

_____

2. Have you been able to look back to identify areas of fear that held you back from living a blessed life as God intended? What has been the change to where you are now? Meditate on areas that may still have hooks into your spirit and focus on severing those tethers.

_____

_____

_____

_____

_____

WHAT HAS GOD SAID TO YOU?

Any time we surrender ourselves to the Holy Spirit, there is inspiration or revelation. Has God spoken into your life as you've studied this session? If so, make sure to write it out so you will have a record of His Word and something real to pray over in the coming days.

_____

_____

_____

_____

_____

CALL TO ACTION

Who do you have in your life that speaks powerful words of affirmation? Have you ever considered giving someone complete authority to speak uninhibited into your life?

_____

_____

_____

_____

_____

SHARE YOUR HEART

Take this time to pray about your relationship with God in in this season of your life. Write out your prayer requests, praise reports and anything you want to step out in faith about. This is your workbook, so write what is on your heart.

_____

_____

_____

_____

_____

_____

_____

_____

_____

_____

_____

_____

_____

_____

_____

_____

_____

_____

_____

_____

_____

_____

_____

_____

_____

_____

Meeting Oz

The Boldness to Ask

Session Seven

DISCUSSION

We began this journey to discover our authority for praying down the power of heaven. Too often we get distracted or redirected before realizing our God-ordained appointment with heaven's blessings. Similarly, Dorothy starts out her journey singing songs with joy and filling each person she encounters with hope. However, when they finally meet Oz, they are immediately frightened by his theatrics that show a voice of anger and thunder roaring and are too scared to be bold.

Do you ever feel that way when coming to God? From the mouths of men, we hear all these things about how God is harsh and how we should fear Him. A lot of us have an unhealthy fear of God because we were told things like "wait till your father gets home" when we were growing up. The association occurs because our earthly father was designed to mirror our heavenly Father. Unfortunately in many cases, that has run off the rails and left us with a crooked impression of our loving God.

We always paint a picture that the Father is going to get us whenever we do something wrong. Seldom do others present a reality of the One who loves us and gives direction, wisdom, and understanding. The problem occurs because we're not approaching God in a one-on-one relationship. We allow others to direct our paths that can lead to a dusty trail instead of a yellow brick road.

How much about God are you willing to believe from the mouths of man? Wouldn't you rather know Him for yourself?

I mean, church is important because we need the Body of Christ to come together as God designed it, but if we do not have an accurate, personal understanding of God as our Father, we will never know our place or position as His kids.

This is the perfect time for you to stick to the path, follow the light and grow an incredibly intimate connection with the one who created you. Seriously, this isn't an old movie on late-night cable television.

We're talking about a tangible relationship with God the Father. He loves you, adores you and has streets of gold waiting to pave your path if only you will allow Him to guide your steps.

RELATED SCRIPTURES

Be strong and very courageous. Be careful to obey all the law my servant Moses gave you; do not turn from it to the right or to the left, that you may be successful wherever you go.
Joshua 1:7

And whatever you ask in prayer, you will receive, if you have faith."
Matthew 21:22

LESSON

Fill in the blanks from Pastor Juan's teaching taken from Session 7:

1. A lot of us have an unhealthy _____ of God because we were told things like "wait till your father gets home" when we were growing up. We always paint a picture that the _____ is going to get us whenever we do something wrong, never a picture of One who loves us and gives direction, wisdom, and understanding.

2. How much about _____ are you willing to believe from the mouths of man?

3. The _____ is also referred to as water, and it is powerful enough to _____ the wicked and all evil.

ADDITIONAL NOTES FROM SESSION SEVEN

Take this opportunity to pray over and think about what was shared in this lesson. Reading is informational but meditating over what was read becomes transformational. Write out your thoughts, observations and questions that may have come up during the lesson.

Go back through the chapter or keep this on hand as you work through the book. The time you invest in prayer will also reveal the answers or clarity that you may seek for very personal questions.

DISCUSSION QUESTIONS

1. When was the last time you were bold in your request to God because of the blood of Jesus that covers you? Describe what made you feel bold and how being bold made you feel.

_____

_____

_____

_____

_____

2. It's been said that people are anxious to improve their circumstances, but are unwilling to improve themselves; therefore, they remain bound. We want, but we won't. Are you willing to weather the storm? Will you commit to stand behind the protection of Jesus Christ as the winds rage against you? Write out your promise to do whatever God asks so that you not only survive the storm but thrive by calling down the promises of God.

_____

_____

_____

_____

_____

WHAT HAS GOD SAID TO YOU?

Any time we surrender ourselves to the Holy Spirit, there is inspiration or revelation. Has God spoken into your life as you've studied this session? If so, make sure to write it out so you will have a record of His Word and something real to pray over in the coming days.

_____

_____

_____

_____

_____

CALL TO ACTION

What do you need God to do in your life at this very moment? Is it money, health, safety, relationship? Stop hiding among the rocky soil and join God on the yellow brick road by praying your petitions with full humility and expectancy.

_____

_____

_____

_____

_____

SHARE YOUR HEART

Take this time to pray about your relationship with God in in this season of your life. Write out your prayer requests, praise reports and anything you want to step out in faith about. This is your workbook, so write what is on your heart.

_____

_____

_____

_____

_____

_____

_____

_____

_____

_____

_____

_____

_____

_____

_____

_____

_____

_____

_____

_____

_____

_____

_____

_____

_____

_____

_____

Get Wrapped

Do you want to get wrapped with Jesus? Here's where you begin your own walk along streets of gold.

Getting Saved

If you want to get right with God, here is a sample prayer. Remember, saying this prayer or any other prayer will not save you, and neither will raising your hand or going down the aisle to an altar.

Surrendering your heart to Jesus Christ is the only way. But let's start somewhere like reading this prayer:

"God, I know that I have sinned against You and am deserving of your wrath. But your son, Jesus Christ, died on the cross and took the punishment that I deserve, so that through faith in Him, I could be forgiven. I place my trust in You for salvation. Thank You for Your grace and forgiveness—and the gift of eternal life! In Jesus's name, Amen!"

He asked for your hand in marriage, and you said YES! Congratulations.

Remember earlier in the book I told you it takes a lifetime to manufacture a saint?

Okay, so now the work begins, but it will be worth it. Jesus is the groom, and everything about Christianity is about becoming one with your spouse. He goes with me everywhere I go, but everywhere I go, I go with Him in my heart.

Begin your journey by getting connected with a body of believers (church) and allow him to order your steps by way of His Word. Meditate on them day and night, and you will be blessed in all that you do.

These are beautiful verses to get you started:

- "For God so loved the world that he gave his one and only Son, that whoever believes in him shall not perish but have eternal life" (John 3:16).

- "Believe in the Lord Jesus, and you will be saved" (Acts 16:31).

- God has already done all of the work. All you must do is receive, in faith, the salvation God offers (Ephesians 2:8-9).

Session Lesson Answer Key

Session 1 – ANSWERS
1. Speak life
2. transforms
3. testimony / proof / overcame

Session 2 – ANSWERS
1. Mess / promise
2. storm / not
3. God's

Session 3 – ANSWERS
1. Bible
2. Perspective / truth
3. Focus / you

Session 4 – ANSWERS
1. Words / colors
2. Believers / promises
3. Devil / fear

Session 5 – ANSWERS
1. storms
2. earth / eternity
3. good / creation

Session 6 – ANSWERS
1. Pray / God
2. Damascus / horse
3. dramatic / purpose

Session 7 – ANSWERS
1. fear / Father
2. God / man
3. Word of God / destroy

About Pastor Juan Martinez

Juan Martinez is the founder of Wrapped in the Love of Christ Ministry and Love Live lead ministries serves as the senior pastor of the Get Wrapped Church in Spring, Texas, since 2010, the ministry has seen thousands of people say yes to Christ. Juan's heart and focus is simply winning souls by wrapping them in the love of Christ.

Through dynamic ministering of the Word of God, Juan is a true revivalist with a burning passion and a deep desire to see the lost saved, the broken mended, the afflicted healed, and the body of Christ operate in its God-given authority.

God has transformed him from having a killing, stealing, and destroying mentality to a seed-sowing mindset, spreading the Good News to all who will listen. He has seen God move miraculously in his life and has a hunger for all of creation to experience the same.

Additionally, Juan is involved in speaking at various conferences and has appeared on many televised programs and is the author of Beyond The Yellow Brick Road. Juan and his wife, Ruthy, have six children: Janina, Valery, Jonathan, Jay, Johnathan, and Joshua.

Beyond The Yellow Brick Road: Unlocking the Promises of God Leader Guide

Help others to learn how to unlock the promises of God by serving as a small group leader. This leader guide gives you the tools to walk through Pastor Juan Martinez's powerful and beautifully written Beyond the Yellow Brick Road: Unlocking the Promises of God which is featured on YouVersion's Bible App!

The study guide is the perfect companion for believers looking to understand God's promises of heaven's blessing. You are serving the kingdom by helping others unlock those very promises.

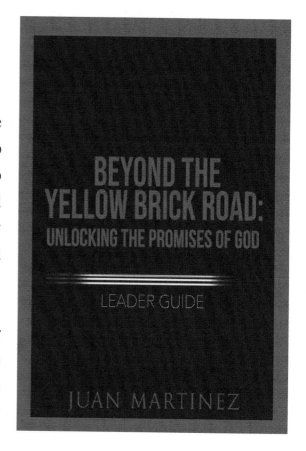

This Leader Guide is best used in conjunction with Pastor Juan's main book, Beyond the Yellow Brick Road: Unlocking the Promises of God and the Study Guide. All three resources can be purchased separately or together at Amazon's book store.

Beyond The Yellow Brick Road:
Unlocking the Promises of God

Pastor Juan Martinez of Get Wrapped Church gives you the keys for unlocking the promises of God in beyond the yellow brick road. After he and his wife, Ruthy, escaped with the clothes on their backs during Hurricane Harvey in 2017, God blessed him with a Wizard of Oz related revelation.

Pastor Juan discovered that the storms in life will reveal truths beyond the yellow brick road and connect us to God's promises of heaven.

This dynamic pastor peppers Holy Spirit truths with honest insights about his struggles from New York's street life, to hard time in the Texas prison system, to a radical transformation that saved his life and launched an impassioned ministry that's leading the lost to meaningful relationships with Christ. Get Wrapped and experience the powerful miracles God has waiting for you.

This Study Guide is best used in conjunction with Pastor Juan's main book, Beyond the Yellow Brick Road: Unlocking the Promises of God and the Leader Guide. All three resources can be purchased separately or together at Amazon's book store.

YouVersion's Bible App
Featured 7-Day Devotional

Based on Pastor Juan's bestselling book, ***Beyond The Yellow Brick Road: Unlocking the Promises of God,*** YouVersion's Bible App offers a free 7-day prayer devotional. Subscribe today!

Pastor Juan Martinez gives you the keys for unlocking God's promises. After escaping with his life during 2017's Hurricane Harvey, God blessed him with a Wizard-of-Oz-related revelation for unlocking the promises of heaven.

From New York's streets to hard time in Texas prisons leading to a radical transformation that launched an impassioned ministry, Pastor Juan shares God's message for powerful prayer in the midst of storms.

Made in the USA
Columbia, SC
25 August 2021